Introduction

C000146066

Visitors to the Falkland Islands have often commented on the lack of a simple means of identifying the local wild flowers. This is so whether their stay be of a long or short duration and whether they be serious wildlife enthusiasts or simply enjoying the natural beauty of the countryside.

Serious botanists must refer to Professor D.M. Moore's two definitive publications – 'The Vascular Flora of the Falkland Islands', *Scientific Reports* No. 60, *British Antarctic Survey*, London (1968) and his 'Flora of Tierra del Fuego', Anthony Nelson, England (1983). The latter has excellent line drawings by Natalie Goodall and covers 90% of the Falklands' flora.

Most visitors only need a simple illustrated guide which, while not claiming to provide the comprehensive coverage of Moore's two floras, would simplify the identification of plants most likely to be encountered.

The advantage of a small, compact, illustrated guide is that each time an unfamiliar flower or plant is found it is relatively easy to scan the pages until a corresponding illustration is found. For those who prefer a more systematic approach a simple key has been devised to facilitate more rapid identification. Please remember that many of the plants described in this book are uncommon and should not be picked indiscriminately.

Vegetation of the Falkland Islands

"An undulating land, with a desolate and wretched aspect is everywhere covered by a peaty soil and wiry grass of one monotonous brown colour" – so wrote Charles Darwin on his visit in 1833.

It is hoped that this book will show the reader that Darwin's opinion was rather harsh and among the "wiry grass and . . . monotonous brown colour" there is a wealth of attractive, colourful plants waiting to be found.

The nomenclature for the vegetation classification presented conforms to the description given in Moore's definitive flora (1968) and the main associations are listed and briefly described below.

1. Maritime tussock formation is confined to coastal areas and is dominated by stands of the tall tussac grass (*Parodiochloa flabellata*) which can grow to 3-4 metres in protected sites. It is now less widespread than previously due to overgrazing, fires, pests and disease. Associated plants are the wild celery (*Apium graveolens*), chickweed (*Stellaria media*) several other grasses, sedges and where the tussac peat has been eroded to give bare surfaces, sorrel (*Rumex acetosella*)   [PLATE 1]

PLATE   1   Maritime tussock formation with tussac grass (*Parodiochloa flabellata*)

T.H. Davies

2. Oceanic heath formation covers most of the Falklands Islands in some form or other. For convenience this community can be sub-divided into grass heath which is dominated by whitegrass (*Cortaderia pilosa*) and dwarf shrub heath dominated by diddle-dee (*Empetrum rubrum*) though a wide degree of intermixing occurs.

(i) Grass heath. Whitegrass dominated vegetation covers the largest area of mainland Falkland Islands. In the better drained more fertile valleys it forms 'bogs' or tussocks whereas on the wet, poorly drained flats it adopts a more lax, less tufted habit. Pigvine (*Gunnera magellanica*), *Pratia* and chickweed are common in the former situation whereas on the wetter sites, sedges, rushes and oreob (*Oreobolus obtusangulus*) are common.   [PLATE 2]

(ii) Dwarf shrub heath is dominated by diddle-dee growing on hard peat overlying rocky ridges or better subsoil. The two *Blechnum* ferns and balsam bog (*Bolax gummifera*) are often found in this situation. Of the more attractive and noticeable plants, *Azorella*, pale maiden (*Sisyrinchium jubatum*), scurvy grass (*Oxalis enneaphylla*) and mountain berry (*Pernettya pumila*) are common. The tall fern (*Blechnum magellanicum*) can assume dominance on rocky areas, particularly on slopes where its dense litter discourages most other plants. The dog orchid (*Codonorchis lessonii*), violet (*Viola maculata*) and almond flower (*Luzuriaga marginata*) can, however, also be found in this situation. On higher damper ground, diddle-dee and mountain berry tend to be co-dominant.   [PLATE 3]

PLATE 3 Dwarf shrub heath community with diddle-dee (*Empetrum rubrum*) and tall fern (*Blechnum magellanicum*)

PLATE 2 Grass heath community with whitegrass (*Cortaderia pilosa*) dominant

J. McAdam

T.H. Davies

3. Feldmark formation dominated by cushion plants such as balsam bog and *Azorella* with both of the common ferns and some grasses is found more commonly on the higher hills and ridges than at lower altitudes. The combination of thin shaley soil, shallow peat, strong winds and generally poorer conditions for plant growth all combine to give these high-altitude areas their characteristic vegetation.   [PLATE 4]

PLATE   4   Feldmark formation dominated by cushion plants

J. McAdam

4. Bog formation This is a variable class of vegetation often comprising wet, swampy areas of short rushes or dense carpets of *Astelia* with low, flat cushions of oreob. The hard surface of this vegetation disguises deep saturated peat with a water table only several centimetres below the surface. This can be a valuable hunting ground for the botanist with interesting plants like the sundew (*Drosera uniflora*) and the little, odd-shaped *Pratia* being found. On damp, level, boggy ground near streams various short rushes are abundant with plants such as the buttercup (*Ranunculus trullifolius*), blinks (*Montia fontana*), *Lilaeopsis macloviana* and the pimpernel (*Anagallis alternifolia*) common.   [PLATE 5]

5. Fresh-water vegetation There are numerous ponds, lakes and streams where blinks, starwort (*Callitriche antarctica*), native water-milfoil (*Myriophyllum elatinoides*), arrow-leaved marigold (*Caltha sagittata*) and willow herb (*Epilobium ciliatum*) are the most frequently occurring plants.   [PLATE 6]

PLATE 5 Bog formation with a dense
              carpet of *Astelia pumila*

PLATE 6 Fresh-water vegetation

J. McAdam

J. McAdam

7

The Wild Flowers of the Falkland Islands

Notes on the flora

Although there are only about 163 native plants recorded from the Falklands, the flora is much more diverse than that of many other South Atlantic and sub-Antarctic islands (eg. Tristan da Cunha and South Georgia). Almost 90% (144 species) of the native species are also found on the South American mainland south of latitude 40° S and almost 80% of the Falkland Islands' flora is recorded from Tierra del Fuego. Approximately 20% (33 species) of the native flora of the Falkland Islands occurs in some part or other of the sub-Antarctic zone, New Zealand or south-eastern Australia. Most of these species (20) are found on the island of South Georgia with the number of species on other places generally decreasing in line with their distance from the Falkland Islands.

At present there are almost 100 alien (introduced) species, most of which have come from Europe and it is estimated that 16% are now widespread in the local vegetation whilst the rest are confined to gardens and settlement paddocks. It is interesting to note that many of these species were also the first to invade many other southern temperate islands following man's initial visits. They are mainly the common weeds of the Northern Hemisphere such as docks, thistles, dandelions and daisies. As they will be familiar to most visitors to the Islands many are not included in this guide.

Due to the limitations of space and the necessity to keep this guide relatively simple, only 61 of the wild flowers (including 2 ferns, 4 grasses and 3 rushes) are described. These species are among the most likely to be encountered while walking in the 'Camp' (countryside) or on the coast.

A simple classification

Most visitors are likely to visit the Islands during the mid-summer period when many of the plants described in this key will be in flower.

The key is based on form or type, with the conspicuously flowering plants further classified by flower type and colour. Where appropriate, some species are included under several sections in the key.

To use the key, first decide whether the plant is a FERN (usually bearing complex fronds from an underground rhizome); a low, compact, dense CUSHION PLANT; an obvious SHRUB OR BUSH; has bright conspicuous BERRIES; is a CONSPICUOUSLY FLOWERING PLANT; is a GRASS or a RUSH.

The main group described is that comprising plants with conspicuous flowers and here the key is based on the size and grouping of the flowers. If the flowers are large and generally solitary, then the rest of the key is based on the number of petals present and their colour. If the flowers are small and grouped into heads, then the shape of the flower head, its likeness to common flowers and its petal colour form the basis of the rest of the key.

SUMMARY KEY TO THE MORE COMMON WILD FLOWERS

FERNS

CUSHION PLANTS

SHRUBS OR BUSHES

BERRIED PLANTS

CONSPICUOUSLY FLOWERING PLANTS

		Colour
Individual flowers large or obviously visible	Curiously shaped flower	White
		Yellow
	Two petals	White
	Four petals	White
	Five petals	White
		White/Lilac
		Yellow
		Pink
	More than five petals	White
		Yellow
	Petals absent	White/Green
Individual flowers small, in heads or spikes	Globular heads	White
		Yellow/Green
		Red
		Pink
	Clover-like head	White
	Daisy-like flowers	White
		Yellow
		White/Mauve
	Dandelion-like flowers	Yellow
		Orange/Red
	Flowers on leafless spikes	Green
	Flat head of small flowers	White

GRASSES

RUSHES

COMPLETE KEY TO THE MORE COMMON WILD FLOWERS

	Common name	Botanical name	Guide No
FERNS	Small fern	*Blechnum penna-marina*	1
	Tall fern	*Blechnum magellanicum*	2
CUSHION PLANTS	Balsam bog	*Bolax gummifera*	3
		Astelia pumila	4
	Oreob	*Oreobolus obtusangulus*	5
		Azorella caespitosa	6
		Nassauvia gaudichaudii	7
SHRUBS OR BUSHES	Native box	*Hebe elliptica*	8
	Gorse	*Ulex europaea*	9
	Fachine	*Chiliotrichum diffusum*	10
BERRIED PLANTS	Diddle-dee	*Empetrum rubrum*	11
	Mountain berry	*Pernettya pumila*	12
	Tea berry	*Myrteola nummularia*	13
	Pig vine	*Gunnera magellanica*	14
		Nertera depressa	15
	Native strawberry	*Rubus geoides*	16

CONSPICUOUSLY FLOWERING PLANTS

Individual flowers large or obviously visible

Curiously shaped flower

		Common name	Botanical name	Guide No
	White	Dog orchid	*Codonorchis lessonii*	17
	Yellow	Lady's slipper	*Calceolaria fothergillii*	18
Two petals				
	White	Eyebright	*Euphrasia antarctica*	19
Four petals				
	White	Bitter cress	*Cardamine glacialis*	20
		Stonecrop	*Crassula moschata*	21
		Tea berry	*Myrteola nummularia*	13
Five petals				
	White	Mouse-eared chickweed	*Cerastium arvense*	22
		Sundew	*Drosera uniflora*	23
		Strawberry	*Rubus geoides*	16
		Field pansy	*Viola arvensis*	24
			Lilaeopsis macloviana	25
		Dusty miller	*Primula magellanica*	26
	White/ Lilac		*Pratia repens*	27
	Yellow	Violet	*Viola maculata*	28
		Buttercup	*Ranunculus trullifolius*	29
	Pink	Pimpernel	*Anagallis alternifolia*	30

More than five petals

	White	Scurvy grass	*Oxalis enneaphylla*	31
		Almond flower	*Luzuriaga marginata*	32
		Pale maiden	*Sisyrinchium jubatum*	33
	Yellow	Arrow-leaved marigold	*Caltha sagittata*	34

Petals absent

	White/ Green		*Colobanthus quitensis*	35

Individual flowers small, in heads or spikes

Globular heads

	White		*Nassauvia serpens*	36
		Dusty miller	*Primula magellanica*	26
	Red	Prickly burr	*Acaena magellanica*	37
	Yellow/ Green		*Cotula scariosa*	38
	Pink	Pimpernel	*Anagallis alternifolia*	30
		Thrift	*Armeria macloviana*	39

Clover-like head

	White	White clover	*Trifolium repens*	40

Daisy-like flowers

	White	Daisy	*Bellis perennis*	41
		Fachine	*Chiliotrichum diffusum*	10
		Christmas bush	*Baccharis magellanica*	42
		Marsh daisy	*Aster vahii*	43
		Vanilla daisy	*Leuceria suaveolens*	44
	Yellow	Sea cabbage	*Senecio candicans*	45
		Groundsel	*Senecio vulgaris*	46
			Senecio littoralis	47
	White/ Mauve	Lavender	*Perezia recurvata*	48
		Cudweed	*Gnaphalium affine*	49

Dandelion-like flowers

	Yellow	Dandelion	*Taraxacum officinale*	50
	Orange/ Red	Orange hawkweed	*Hieracium aurantiacum*	51

Flowers in leafless spikes

	Green	Sheep's sorrel	*Rumex acetosella*	52
		Curled dock	*Rumex crispus*	53

Flat head of small flowers

	White	Wild celery	*Apium graveolens*	54

GRASSES		Whitegrass	*Cortaderia pilosa*	55
		Cinnamon grass	*Hierochloe redolens*	56
		Tussac grass	*Parodiochloa flabellata*	57
			Poa robusta	58

RUSHES		Native rush	*Juncus scheuzerioides*	59
		Short rush	*Rostkovia magellanica*	60
		Tall rush	*Marsippospermum grandiflorum*	61

11

Description of the species

The brief description given supplements the photograph of each species which will be the main identification tool used in this book. For most of the plants only a few notes on particular characteristics and the type of habitat where the plant might be found are given. However some of the species are extremely attractive, locally popular, or have some interesting historical associations and merit a longer note.

FERNS

1. Small fern (*Blechnum penna – marina*)

Common in all communities, particularly on damper ground. It can form dense carpets, the fronds emerging as a dull, ruddy-brown in spring developing into a dark glossy green. [PLATE 7]

PLATE 7 Small fern (*Blechnum penna-marina*)

A. Douse

2. Tall fern (*Blechnum magellanicum*)

This stout, coarse fern can form huge, dense clumps or 'beds' of live and dead fronds on drier diddle-dee heath and among rocks on the hillsides. Young fronds have a distinct bronze colour which later turns to dark green. Abundant throughout the Falklands. [PLATE 8]

PLATE 8 Tall fern (*Blechnum magellanicum*)

T.H. Davies

CUSHION PLANTS

3. Balsam bog (*Bolax gummifera*)

The balsam bog comprises a hard cushion of densely packed rosettes which can form huge mounds. In open, sunny positions the cushions are a pale yellowish green. In shade, the plant forms a looser cushion often of a darker green colour. It is repeated branching of the shoots which leads to the dense cushion-like form and which caused the famous botanist Hooker to write " . . . the little branches being so tightly packed together that they present an even surface, of such hardness and compactness that the knuckles may be broken against the mass". They are called balsam bogs from the fragrant and resinous smell of the white gum which exudes from between the rosettes and hardens into reddish brown blobs on the surface. Abundant, particularly in rocky areas on shaley soil.   [PLATE 9]

PLATE   9   Balsam bog (*Bolax gummifera*)

T.H. Davies

4. *Astelia pumila*

Forms bright green, hard sheets or low flat cushions on deep waterlogged peat [See also Plate 5]. The leaves are sharp pointed and very stiff to the touch. *Astelia* is widespread over wet areas in the Islands and is typical of what is traditionally known as 'soft camp'. [PLATE 10]

5. Oreob (*Oreobolus obtusangulus*)

A densely tufted, fine-leaved little herb forming low (5-10 cm) cushions which are 10-25 cm in diameter. Found in the wetter grassland areas (with whitegrass) or in association with *Astelia* (4). [PLATE 11]

A. Douse

PLATE 10   *Astelia pumila*

J. McAdam

PLATE 11   Oreob
(*Oreobolus obtusangulus*) – centre

6. *Azorella caespitosa*

There are four species of *Azorella* found in the Falklands. All are cushion plants with *Azorella caespitosa* forming the largest cushions and *A. lycopodioides* being the most abundant. This species forms low, spreading cushions under 10 cm tall which can be very "loose" and is found in all communities, particularly shrub heath.　　　　[PLATES 12 and 13]

PLATE 12 *Azorella caespitosa*

J. McAdam

PLATE 13 *Azorella* – complete cushion

T.H. Davies

7. *Nassauvia gaudichaudii*

This most appealing plant forms low cushions or dense carpets up to a metre across. The small bright green leaves on the surface are spined and sparsely hairy at the margins while the stems below are woody and clothed with old dead leaves.

The heavily scented, solitary flowers consisting of 3 to 5 cream coloured florets are produced in profusion, often hiding the leaves beneath. The stamens are brown.

Though common in the Falkland Islands this plant does not occur elsewhere. Its preferred habitat is amongst rocks or sand near the coast but it can sometimes be found in poorly developed dwarf shrub heath or even in whitegrass. [PLATE 14]

PLATE 14 *Nassauvia gaudichaudii*

T.H. Davies

SHRUBS OR BUSHES

8. Native box (*Hebe elliptica*)

One of the tallest native plants on the Islands and one which, by all accounts, used to be much more common than it is today. Box is commonly used as a hedging plant around gardens in Stanley and the outlying settlements and it can grow up to 3 m tall. In the wild it tends to be found on rocky areas around the coast on West Falkland or remote islands where it is relatively protected from sheep and cattle.   [PLATE 15]

PLATE 15 Native box (*Hebe elliptica*)

J. McAdam

9. Gorse (*Ulex europea*)

A dense spiny bush with bright yellow flowers which was introduced from Europe by the early settlers for use as hedges to contain cattle. It can be found around most settlements or where there is any history of habitation. [PLATE 16]

10. Fachine (*Chiliotrichum diffusum*)

From early accounts it is clear that fachine used to be much more widespread throughout the Islands than today. This bushy plant can reach 2 m tall and has striking dark green leaves with a white, hairy underside. The large attractive flowers are up to 3 cm in diameter. Fachine is most commonly found along the banks of streams or in areas where grazing pressures are very light (eg. in horse paddocks). [PLATE 17]

PLATE 16 Gorse (*Ulex europea*) hedge, West Point Island

PLATE 17 Fachine (*Chiliotrichum diffusum*) – bushes in flower

J. McAdam

J. McAdam

19

BERRIED PLANTS

11. Diddle-dee (*Empetrum rubrum*)

One of the most common plants in the Islands, diddle-dee is often the dominant species on dry "hard camp". It is a small shrub with red berries. The berries are eaten in large quantities by birds and are locally made into jams, jellies and tarts. They are not sweet but have a distinctive flavour which produces an astringent effect on the mouth. The leaves and twigs are resinous and therefore burn readily, even when wet. [PLATE 18]

PLATE 18 Diddle-dee (*Empetrum rubrum*)

M. Morrison

12. Mountain berry (*Pernettya pumila*)

A creeping shrub reaching up to 60 cm in length with dark green shiny, slightly pointed leaves. The small white bell-shaped flowers [Plate 19] generally point downwards and the round, reddish-white berry [Plate 20] which can be tinged with purple is up to 12 mm across. Common throughout the Islands in most communities.   [PLATES 19 and 20]

PLATE 19 Mountain berry
(*Pernettya pumila*) – flowers

B. Summers

PLATE 20 Mountain berry – fruits

M. Morrison

21

13. Tea berry (*Myrteola nummularia*)

This plant derives its name from its leaves which the early settlers dried and used as a form of tea. It is a creeping shrub found only on deeper peat areas and has a very sweet, distinctly flavoured berry [see also Plate 63]. The plant is prostrate and the berries tedious to pick, making a bowl of tea berries and cream a well earned treat. [PLATES 21 and 22]

14. Pig vine (*Gunnera magellanica*)

A creeping, branched herb with kidney shaped, rhubarb-like leaves which are smooth above, hairy below and commonly 3-8 cm wide. Following flowering in November a tight bunch of brilliant scarlet fruits is borne on short stalks. Pig vine is abundant throughout the camp, particularly in damp sheltered places. [PLATE 23]

M. Morrison

J. Spruce

PLATE 21 Tea berry
(*Myrteola nummularia*) – fruits

PLATE 22 Tea berry – flowers

J. McAdam

PLATE 23 Pig vine (*Gunnera magellanica*)

22

15. *Nertera depressa*

A graceful creeping herb with stems up to 50 cm long and small, (about 6 mm) bright green, slightly succulent, rounded leaves. Surprisingly this plant has no local name though it is very common in damp areas, particularly in rocky areas near the sea. It can form dense mats and has a very conspicuous globular, bright red berry. [PLATE 24]

16. Native strawberry (*Rubus geoides*)

The red distinctive berry of the native strawberry resembles a raspberry but has a distinct and delicious flavour, something between that of a strawberry and raspberry. It is a low straggling plant with a slightly woody stem, toothed leaves (12-30 mm long) and attractive white six-petalled flowers. The fruit, which grow tight on the ground, is best found in January and February. [PLATE 25]

PLATE 24 *Nertera depressa*

PLATE 25 Native strawberry (*Rubus geoides*)

S. Wolsey

M. Morrison

CONSPICUOUSLY FLOWERING PLANTS

17. Dog orchid (*Codonorchis lessonii*)

The dog orchid is the commonest of the four species of orchid found in the Falklands. It is a delicate plant, 10-25 cm tall with a whorl of about 3 shiny green leaves clasping the reddish brown stem at or below its middle. The variable white flower, which has purplish tinges and a pleasant scent, appears before Christmas. The dog orchid is not uncommon, though its frequency can vary from season to season and it is best found in whitegrass and diddle-dee heath, particularly where the plant cover is sparse. [PLATE 26]

18. Lady's slipper (*Calceolaria fothergillii*)

The beautiful yellow flower of lady's slipper is borne on a short (10 cm) stalk arising from a basal rosette of 2 cm long, hairy, spoon-shaped leaves. The pure white bar across the 'pouch' and purple-red striping in the 'throat' and across the 'lip' make this flower one of the most attractive to be found in the Islands. It grows on coastal slopes amongst open dwarf shrub heath in well drained light sandy soil and where the peat cover is thin. It tends to occur in colonies of no more than a few dozen plants and, although widespread, is not common. [PLATE 27]

PLATE 26 Dog orchid (*Codonorchis lessonii*)

PLATE 27 Lady's slipper (*Calceolaria fothergillii*)

M. Morrison

T.H. Davies

24

19. Antarctic eyebright (*Euphrasia antarctica*)

A small (less than 3 cm) hairy plant with 3-lobed wedge shaped leaves shielding an attractive little flower. The white petals have a dark violet streak and the back of the flower is a deep golden yellow. Although inconspicuous and uncommon, eyebright is worth looking out for during January and February in damp coastal areas by streams and pools and between sand dunes. [PLATE 28]

20. Bittercress (*Cardamine glacialis*)

A very variable plant with stems 15-30 cm and pinnate (toothed or fern-like) dark green leaves. The four-petalled 'crucifer' flower is small, white and borne during November and December. It is reasonably common in most moist areas, particularly near the coast.

PLATE 28   Antarctic eyebright (*Euphrasia antarctica*)

J. McAdam

25

21. Stonecrop (*Crassula moschata*)

A small, succulent herb with banana-shaped, fleshy leaves forming extensive patches on moist sandy and rocky shores, often near the high water mark. The tiny white or pinkish flowers can be found throughout the summer. [PLATE 29]

22. Mouse-eared chickweed (*Cerastium arvense*)

The white flowers of chickweed composed of 5 deeply lobed petals are often seen dotted through the drier whitegrass or diddle-dee camp. The somewhat straggling, branched stems can reach up to 20 cm and occasionally form loose mats. [PLATE 30]

PLATE 29 Stonecrop (*Crassula moschata*)

A. Douse

PLATE 30 Mouse-eared chickweed (*Cerastium arvense*)

A. Douse

26

23. Sundew (*Drosera uniflora*)

The tiny leaves of the insectiverous sundew with their sticky globular red hairs can be commonly found on wet, mossy areas, *Astelia* bogs [Plate 5] or on open peat. The whole plant is less than 4 cm tall and the white to green flowers, borne on a single stalk arising from the centre of the basal rosette of leaves, are surprisingly large (8 mm) for the small plant. [PLATE 31]

24. Field pansy (*Viola arvensis*)

The common European field pansy is naturalised in the Falklands where it is commonly found near settlements, particularly where the ground has been disturbed or cultivated. An annual plant, growing up to 40 cm tall with hairy stems, variable leaves and cream coloured petals, though the upper petal can often be violet-bluish in colour.

PLATE 31 Sundew (*Drosera uniflora*) – centre with flowers

T.H. Davies

27

25. *Lilaeopsis macloviana*

The tiny white 5-petalled flowers of this spreading much-branched prostrate herb often pepper the ground surface on mud, wet sand or around the margins of ponds and streams.

The leaves are rush-like and fleshy with clear internal divisions (or septae) and are borne in clumps at the nodes of the white fleshy stems. *Lilaeopsis* is only found in the Falkland Islands where it is fairly common though difficult to find when not in flower. [PLATE 32]

26. Dusty miller (*Primula magellanica*)

Dusty miller, a charming and favourite wild flower in the Falklands, grows as a loose rosette of spoon-shaped leaves with toothed margins. The flower stalk is often short, but can be up to 20 cm tall and the white primrose-like flowers, each with a yellow eye, form a dense, spherical head. Once believed to have been very common it is more restricted now, though in spring (Oct-Nov) its flowers can be found in sandy, well-drained open dwarf shrub heath and short turf from sea level to the highest peaks. [PLATE 33]

PLATE 32 *Lilaeopsis macloviana*   PLATE 33 Dusty miller (*Primula magellanica*)

J. McAdam

B. Summers

27. *Pratia repens*

A short (5 cm) creeping, slender herb with kidney shaped, wavy edged leaves which forms dense mats in moist places, particularly on peat banks. *Pratia* is best recognised by its rather odd lilac or white flowers which are borne in December and have 5 'petals' offset to one side of the flower-head leaving a conspicuous gap on the other side.   [PLATE 34]

28. Violet (*Viola maculata*)

Its bright yellow flowerhead consisting of 5 petals make this violet stand out very clearly amongst dry open diddle-dee heath in December on coastal slopes or on sandy areas where it is fairly common. The plant is about 10-15 cm high with oval, toothed, hairy leaves borne on long stalks. The violet is one of the more attractive wild flowers to be found in the Islands yet, despite the bright flower, it is completely odourless.   [PLATE 35]

PLATE 34 *Pratia repens*
– flower and 'round' leaves

PLATE 35 Violet (*Viola maculata*)

29

29. Buttercup (*Ranunculus trullifolius*)

Prevalent around shallow pools or open mud and wet sand beside streams and ponds, this is the commonest of the buttercups found in the Falklands. A creeping plant with stems 8-10 cm long, it has peculiar small fleshy, wedge-shaped, lobed leaves borne on stalks. The yellow flowers are 10 mm across, buttercup-like and borne singly. [PLATE 36]

30. Pimpernel (*Anagallis alternifolia*)

A low-growing, branching, prostrate annual herb with oval fleshy leaves and small, solitary, pale-pink star shaped flowers. The pimpernel flowers in January and is best found in moist places, particularly on sandy ground. [PLATE 37]

J. McAdam

PLATE 36 Buttercup
(*Ranunculus trullifolius*)

J. McAdam

PLATE 37 Pimpernel (*Anagallis alternifolia*)

30

31. Scurvy grass (*Oxalis enneaphylla*)

So-called because it was recognised by early sailors as possessing anti-scorbutic properties. A delicious, refreshing drink is still made from the stalks of this attractive plant. Clayton, who was the commanding officer of the first British settlement at Port Egmont, described in 1773 a "wood sorrel in the spring season . . . they blow a white flower forming a cup and are most like the wild roses which grow in our hedges in England." Clayton's 'wood sorrel' was the beautiful *Oxalis enneaphylla*. It is a delicate little plant with a slender stalk, blue-green leaves and a white or pink trumpet shaped flower. Pernetty, the early French colonist, called it "Vinaigrette" and described it as "exhalant une odeur d'amande très suave". Following the early settlers' practice of making scurvy grass jam the plant is still called scurvy grass locally although it is, of course, not a true grass.

It has simple or branched rhizomes spread to various depths with fleshy scales on the growing points. The silver grey leaflets radiate from the tips of the leaf-stalks and nestling amongst the foliage or carried above it are the large, solitary pearly-white or pink flushed funnel-shaped flowers. Plant size is very variable ranging from a single flower surrounded by a few dwarf leaves in dry situations to multi-flowered trailing growth on shaded banks and damp places. Generally it grows in dwarf shrub heath and is less common in the drier parts of the Islands than near the coast.   [PLATE 38]

PLATE 38 Scurvy grass (*Oxalis enneaphylla*)

J. McAdam

32. Almond flower (*Luzuriaga marginata*)

A spreading or creeping plant which can reach a length of several metres. The elliptical leaves are approximately 12 mm long and lie flat on the ground though the white flowers, borne in November, December and January are the most striking feature of the plant. The six white petals of this charming and most interesting plant are regularly arranged to form a symmetrical cup. The berry is a distinctive deep purple. It grows in dwarf shrub heath at all altitudes but is healthiest in shaded sites, particularly amongst stones and often with balsam bog and mountain berry. Almond flowers can be best found along the edges of stoneruns.   [PLATE 39]

33. Pale maiden (*Sisyrinchium jubatum*)

A rhizomatous perennial which lies dormant in winter and then provides a flush of colour in camp during most of the spring and early summer period. The leaves are stiffly erect, rush-like and usually about 20 cm tall. The two to eight flowers which emerge from a little below the tip open in succession first into pendant bells then later into flatter open cups of pure white, yellow at the base and with purple veins. Pale maidens grow in both dwarf shrub heath and whitegrass heath from the coast up into the hills. It is comparatively common though not as abundant as formerly when the famous botanist J.D. Hooker said of the

PLATE 39 Almond flower
(*Luzuriaga marginata*)

PLATE 40 Pale maiden
(*Sisyrinchium jubatum*)

B. Summers

M. Morrison

plant 'One of the most abundant and elegant plants in the Falkland Islands, where the grass plains are in the spring month of November, almost whitened by the profusion of its pendulous, snowy bells'.

[PLATE 40]

34. Arrow-leaved marigold (*Caltha sagittata*)

Most commonly this plant is seen in a prostrate form growing in short turf on greens near streams and ponds. The succulent, shiny green arrow-shaped leaves and large white-green flowers (10-30 mm) arise from a horizontal, fleshy, creeping rhizome. However the plant is very variable in form. In wet situations, beside or in streams and where the associated vegetation is lush, the rhizome is often ascending and the whole plant becomes stout and tall. Flowering takes place in November and December. The marigold is found on wet sand, shingle and mud beside the sea and freshwater.

[PLATE 41]

35. Pearlwort (*Colobanthus quitensis*)

Pearlwort is commonly found on damp sand, gravel or peat just above the high-water mark and by lakes and rivers inland. The network of stems forms loose mats or cushions several centimetres in diameter bearing a variable number of leafy shoots. The stem carries a club-like flower with no petals and either four or five green, triangular sepals.

PLATE 41 Arrow-leaved marigold (*Caltha sagittata*)

J. McAdam

36. *Nassauvia serpens*

This is quite the most unusual plant of the Falkland Islands both in appearance and habitat. It is normally found only among boulders making up the spectacular stoneruns of the mountains and hills. It does not occur elsewhere in the world.

From roots at the bottom of the stonerun, straggling, branched stems, up to 200 cm or longer, covered in overlapping scale-like leaves ascend to the surface. There they spread to form tangled bushes up to 1 m across of erect stems carrying terminal club-shaped heads of small white florets. The inflorescences are strongly scented and have a pale lavender appearance due to purple stamens in the florets. [PLATE 42]

PLATE 42 *Nassauvia serpens*

T.H. Davies

37. Prickly burr (*Acaena magellanica*)

The prickly burr forms large clumps with straggling, prostrate, reddish stems rising to about 40 cm. The stems, branches and leaf stalks are reddish in colour and the leaves are made up of 4-7 pairs of deeply toothed leaflets. The head is a globule of individual red or reddish-green flowers and each 'fruit' has four spines which readily adhere to clothing and sheep fleece to give the plant its particularly apt name.

Prickly burr is very common among rocks, pebbles and sand near the sea or in whitegrass meadows and moist dwarf shrub heath along streams and near ponds. [PLATE 43]

38. *Cotula scariosa*

The tiny leaves of *Cotula* are almost a miniature version of those of the prickly burr. The plant forms an open network of short (about 10 cm long) straggling stems on marshy ground by streams and on wet sand. Tiny yellowish green flowers which are borne on a short (up to 2 cm) stalk, form a compact head about 8 mm in diameter. This little plant is uncommon and is often overlooked. [PLATE 44]

A. Douse

PLATE 43 Prickly burr (*Acaena magellanica*)

PLATE 44 *Cotula scariosa*

A. Douse

35

39. Thrift (*Armeria macloviana*)

The rose-pink ball of flowers which is distinctive of thrift, can be found amongst rocks and sand along seashores through December and January. Thrift is a stocky plant, about 15 cm high, and has tufts of dark green fleshy leaves with a lighter central vein. [PLATE 45]

40. White clover (*Trifolium repens*)

White clover has creeping branched stems, typically trifoliate 'clover' leaves and a globular head of white or pink flowers borne on a stem of varying length. White clover has been introduced and is fairly common on waste ground near settlements, alongside roads or pathways in Stanley and in some sown or improved pastures. [PLATE 46]

PLATE 45 Thrift (*Armeria macloviana*)

B. Summers

PLATE 46 White clover (*Trifolium repens*)

J. McAdam

41. Daisy (*Bellis perennis*)

The common European daisy has been introduced to the Falklands and is reasonably widespread around settlements, along the coast and in dry pastures which have been hard grazed by sheep. Its typical 'fried egg' flower head and basal rosette of leaves need no further description. [PLATE 47]

42. Christmas bush (*Baccharis magellanica*)

This dwarf evergreen shrub hugs the ground in impoverished sites but in the cover of diddle-dee, where the fertility is better, it can be luxuriant. It has dense, small (about 12 mm long), holly-shaped leaves which are held on short stalks around the stems. The plant can often be covered in yellow-white terminal flower heads during December and January. Christmas bush, probably so called because of its prolific flowering over the festive season, is found in both grass heath and dwarf shrub heath associations and is very common on wet or dry ground throughout the Islands. [PLATE 48]

J. McAdam

PLATE 47 Daisy (*Bellis perennis*)

A. Wright

PLATE 48 Christmas bush
(*Baccharis magellanica*)
with white flowers

37

43. Marsh daisy (*Aster vahlii*)

The marsh daisy is about 20 cm high with a simple erect stem arising from thick rhizomes up to 30 cm long. Its thick leaves are elongated – oval in shape. The large (20-25 mm) flower heads, which emerge during November and December, are at first white and later become tipped with brilliant rose. Although this attractive daisy can be found in damp places in whitegrass heath or on moist sand near the sea, it is less common nowadays than it was in the early part of the century.   [PLATE 49]

44. Vanilla daisy (*Leuceria suaveolens*)

The densely woolly, silvery, basal leaves of the vanilla daisy grow up to 10 cm long from a swollen scale-covered rootstock. The complex and most striking creamy white flowerhead is borne on a hairy stalk up to 25 cm tall and can be seen from late November to early January. Vanilla daisy is found in sunny positions in dwarf shrub heath on well drained peat, especially among rocks and often in association with balsam bogs and tall fern. Only found in the Falklands, vanilla daisy is so named because of its scent.   [PLATE 50]

PLATE 49 Marsh daisy (*Aster vahlii*)

PLATE 50 Vanilla daisy (*Leuceria suaveolens*)

B. Summers

J. McAdam

38

45. Sea cabbage (*Senecio candicans*)

A striking silvery coloured, fleshy leaved luxuriant plant which is found only on the seashore and is quite unlike anything else in the Islands. It grows up to 1 m high from a stout rootstock and the basal leaves have a longer stalk than those borne further up the stem. The yellow flowerheads, borne in umbels (a flat or convex inflorescence) emerge during January. Sea cabbage, so-called because its anti-scorbutic properties were recognised by the early sailors, is absent from only a few sandy beaches in the Falklands. [PLATE 51]

PLATE 51 Sea cabbage (*Senecio candicans*)

T.H. Davies

46. Groundsel (*Senecio vulgaris*)

Groundsel was introduced from Europe and is now fairly widespread throughout the Islands, particularly on areas where the soil has been disturbed or burnt. The yellow, tubular flowers can be found throughout most of the year on stalks 8-45 cm tall and the fleshy leaves are deeply dissected. [PLATE 52]

47. *Senecio littoralis*

This short, much branched woody perennial has both attractive foliage and flowers. The leaves are clothed with woolly hairs to varying degrees giving the plant a generally grey appearance. The ray and disc florets are a clear bright yellow colour. Plants are normally 8 to 25 cm tall and found in well drained dwarf shrub heath usually among rocks. It is endemic to the Falkland Islands. [PLATE 53]

PLATE 52 Groundsel (*Senecio vulgaris*)

PLATE 53 *Senecio littoralis*

J. McAdam

T.H. Davies

40

48. Falkland lavender (*Perezia recurvata*)

The local lavender is one of the most attractive plants in the Islands, forming small clumps or bushes up to 30 cm high. It is commonly found near the sea among rocks, overhanging cliffs, sandy shores or sometimes in coastal dwarf shrub heath. The flowering stems are clothed with tough, dark green, wrinkled, spiny leaves about 20 mm long. The flowers, which can range from white to blue are about 25 mm across and are found during the midsummer months.   [PLATE 54]

49. Cudweed (*Gnaphalium affine*)

Cudweed grows to about 8 cm high and is sparsely covered with woolly hairs. The hairy leaves are 6-12 mm long and the purplish-tipped florets are not particularly obvious though the plant is most likely to be seen in January, near streams, in grass or on heaths. This particular cudweed is found nowhere outside the Falklands.   [PLATE 55]

PLATE 54 Falkland lavender
(*Perezia recurvata*)

PLATE 55 Cudweed
(*Gnaphalium affine*) – centre

J. McAdam

A. Douse

41

50. Dandelion (*Taraxacum officinale*)

The traditional flat, yellow flowerhead (3-6 cm across) of the introduced dandelion can be seen around settlements, in Stanley and on waste ground. It flowers over November, December and January.   [PLATE 56]

51. Orange hawkweed (*Hieracium aurantiacum*)

This hairy leaved plant has distinctive orange-red dandelion-like flowers in January. Being an introduced species and probably a garden escape, it is uncommon in camp but the visitor may encounter dense clumps in gardens and waste ground along the seafront in Stanley – particularly near the Battle Memorial on Ross Road West.   [PLATE 57]

PLATE 56 Dandelion
          (*Taraxacum officinale*)

PLATE 57 Orange hawkweed
          (*Hieracium aurantiacum*)

J. McAdam

J. Spruce

52. Sheep's sorrel (*Rumex acetosella*)

Sheep's sorrel is widely found throughout the Islands on eroded peat or open soil or shingle and on areas which have been cultivated, burned or disturbed. The plant grows up to 30 cm tall and has arrow-shaped acid-tasting leaves which have two characteristic basal lobes. It is most conspicuous in autumn when it becomes brilliant red making spectacular splashes of colour in the otherwise drab camp. [PLATE 58]

PLATE 58 Sheep's sorrel (*Rumex acetosella*)

J. McAdam

43

53. Curled dock (*Rumex crispus*)

This dock growing from 30 cm-100cm tall is occasionally found on shingle beaches. The leaves are about 25 cm long and have curled, twisted and wrinkled margins. [PLATE 59]

54. Wild celery (*Apium graveolens*)

As its name implies the wild celery is a close relative of its cultivated namesake and can be readily identified by its characteristic smell. The oblong leaves have 1-5 pairs of leaflets and the flat, typically umbellifer-like head of small white flowers is borne on a stem of very variable length. Wild celery flowers from November to January and is found in damp places by the coast, particularly in association with tussac grass. [PLATE 60]

PLATE 59 Curled dock (*Rumex crispus*)

PLATE 60 Wild celery (*Apium graveolens*)

GRASSES

55. Whitegrass (*Cortaderia pilosa*)

The most common grass in the Falklands and the main component of 'soft camp', whitegrass gives a large proportion of the Islands' landscape its characteristic 'dun' colour. It is a coarse wiry grass adopting a range of forms in different situations. In sheltered damp, relatively fertile valleys, it can form tussocks whereas on poorly drained, wet, peaty 'flats' it adopts a more lax growth habit. Although whitegrass-dominant vegetation seems monotonous it provides shelter for some inconspicuous but attractive flowers. [PLATE 2]

56. Cinnamon grass (*Hierochlöe redolens*)

Cinnamon grass forms large, lax clumps arising from shortly spreading rhizomes. The broad, glossy-green leaves have a distinct smell when crushed and this gives rise to the plant's name. The flowers and seed head have a silvery sheen until the seed is very ripe. It tends to be found in damp areas, particularly where sheep grazing has been light.

[PLATE 61]

PLATE 61 Cinnamon grass (*Hierochlöe redolens*)

J. McAdam

57. Tussac grass (*Parodiochloa flabellata*)

Tussac derives its name from the huge clumps or 'bogs' it forms which can be up to 3 to 4 metres tall, though 2 metres is more common. From historical evidence there was once a fringe of tussac around the entire Falklands' coastline but due to fires and uncontrolled grazing, tussac is now largely confined to unstocked islands and protected headlands. This grass is of value because of the abundance of leafy growth in summer and its ability to remain winter-green.   [PLATE 62]

58. *Poa robusta*

This grass has stiff prickly leaves forming distinctive, spiky clumps which feel very sharp to the touch. The yellowish flowers and seedhead and the brown tips to the leaves give extensive mats of *Poa robusta* a 'dead' appearance. It is found near the coast, particularly at the head of freshwater creeks, but its most celebrated locality is on the sea wall in front of the Secretariat in Stanley.

PLATE 62 Tussac grass (*Parodiochloa flabellata*)

T.H. Davies

RUSHES

59. Native rush (*Juncus scheuzerioides*)

The native rush is abundant in many areas, particularly on moist sand and among dunes. The plant produces dense tufts of narrow, jointed leaves on a long rhizome. The flowering stem, which bears three to five 'flowers' on a terminal inflorescence in November and December, is often shorter than the leaves which can vary from 2 to 14 cm.   [PLATE 63]

PLATE 63 Native rush (*Juncus scheuzerioides*) with teaberry (centre – in flower)

T.H. Davies

60. Short rush (*Rostkovia magellanica*)

Sometimes called the brown rush, the clusters of fine stems of this plant grow to a height of about 20 cm. The conspicuously channelled leaves are usually larger than the stems. Short rush flowers in October but is best recognised later in the season by its single, shiny brown 'nut'. It is common on damp marshy ground and is frequently found on 'soft' whitegrass camp. [PLATE 64]

61. Tall rush (*Marsippospermum grandiflorum*)

This tall rigid, erect rush has only one obvious leaf per stem. The tall rush is very common, either on 'hard' camp where it is often found with balsam bog and tall fern or on open, moist peaty grassland. The rather ornate flower is borne singly on a stem up to 30 cm tall in November. [PLATE 65]

PLATE 64 Short rush
(*Rostkovia magellanica*)
– nut and leaves

PLATE 65 Tall rush
(*Marsippospermum grandiflorum*)
– flower and leaves

J. McAdam

J. McAdam

48